THE GOSPEL ACCORDING TO
LUKE

Little Rock Scripture Study Staff

LITTLE ROCK SCRIPTURE STUDY

A ministry of the Diocese of Little Rock
in partnership with Liturgical Press

DIOCESE OF LITTLE ROCK

2500 North Tyler Street • P.O. Box 7239 • Little Rock, Arkansas 72217 • (501) 664-0340 • Fax (501) 664-6304

Office of the Bishop

Dear Friends in Christ,

The Bible comes to us as both a gift and an opportunity. It is a gift of God who loves us enough to communicate with us. The only way to enjoy the gift is to open and savor it. The Bible is also an opportunity to actually meet God who is present in the stories, teachings, people, and prayers that fill its pages.

I encourage you to open your Bibles in anticipation that God will do something good in your life. I encourage you to take advantage of the opportunity to meet God in prayer, study, and small-group discussion.

Little Rock Scripture Study offers materials that are simple to use, and a method that has been tested by time. The questions in this study guide will direct your study, help you to understand the passages you are reading, and challenge you to relate the Scriptures to your own life experiences.

Allow the Word of God to form you as a disciple of the Lord Jesus. Accept the challenge to be "transformed by the renewal of your mind" (Romans 12:2). Above all, receive God's Word as his gift, and act upon it.

Sincerely in Christ,

✠ J. Peter Sartain
Bishop of Little Rock

Sacred Scripture

"The Church has always venerated the divine Scriptures just as she venerates the body of the Lord, since from the table of both the word of God and of the body of Christ she unceasingly receives and offers to the faithful the bread of life, especially in the sacred liturgy. She has always regarded the Scriptures together with sacred tradition as the supreme rule of faith, and will ever do so. For, inspired by God and committed once and for all to writing, they impart the word of God Himself without change, and make the voice of the Holy Spirit resound in the words of the prophets and apostles. Therefore, like the Christian religion itself, all the preaching of the Church must be nourished and ruled by sacred Scripture. For in the sacred books, the Father who is in heaven meets His children with great love and speaks with them; and the force and power in the word of God is so great that it remains the support and energy of the Church, the strength of faith for her sons, the food of the soul, the pure and perennial source of spiritual life."

Vatican II, Dogmatic Constitution on Divine Revelation, no. 21.

INTERPRETATION OF SACRED SCRIPTURE

"Since God speaks in sacred Scripture through men in human fashion, the interpreter of sacred Scripture, in order to see clearly what God wanted to communicate to us, should carefully investigate what meaning the sacred writers really intended, and what God wanted to manifest by means of their words.

"Those who search out the intention of the sacred writers must, among other things, have regard for 'literary forms.' For truth is proposed and expressed in a variety of ways, depending on whether a text is history of one kind or another, or whether its form is that of prophecy, poetry, or some other type of speech. The interpreter must investigate what meaning the sacred writer intended to express and actually expressed in particular circumstances as he used contemporary literary forms in accordance with the situation of his own time and culture. For the correct understanding of what the sacred author wanted to assert, due attention must be paid to the customary and characteristic styles of perceiving, speaking, and narrating which prevailed at the time of the sacred writer, and to the customs men normally followed in that period in their everyday dealings with one another."

Vatican II, Dogmatic Constitution on Divine Revelation, no. 12.

Instructions

MATERIALS FOR THE STUDY

This Study Guide: The Gospel According to Luke

Bible: The New American Bible with Revised New Testament or The New Jerusalem Bible is recommended. Paraphrased editions are discouraged as they offer little if any help when facing difficult textual questions. Choose a Bible you feel free to write in or underline.

Commentary: The New Collegeville Bible Commentary, volume 3, *The Gospel According to Luke* by Michael F. Patella, o.s.b. (Liturgical Press) is used with this study. The abbreviations for this commentary, NCBC-NT volume 3, and the assigned pages are found at the beginning of each lesson.

ADDITIONAL MATERIALS

Bible Dictionary: *The Dictionary of the Bible* by John L. McKenzie (Simon & Schuster) is highly recommended as a reference.

Notebook: A notebook may be used for lecture notes and your personal reflections.

WEEKLY LESSONS

Lesson 1—Luke 1
Lesson 2—Luke 2
Lesson 3—Luke 3–5

YOUR DAILY PERSONAL STUDY

The first step is prayer. Open your heart and mind to God. Reading Scripture is an opportunity to listen to God who loves you. Pray that the same Holy Spirit who guided the formation of Scripture will inspire you to correctly understand what you read and empower you to make what you read a part of your life.

The next step is commitment. Daily spiritual food is as necessary as food for the body. This study is divided into daily units. Schedule a regular time and place for your study, as free from distractions as possible. Allow about twenty minutes a day. Make it a daily appointment with God.

As you begin each lesson read the assigned chapters of Scripture found at the beginning of each lesson, the footnotes in your Bible, and then the indicated pages of the commentary. This preparation will give you an overview of the entire lesson and help you to appreciate the context of individual passages.

As you reflect on Scripture, ask yourself these four questions:

1. *What does the Scripture passage say?*
   Read the passage slowly and reflectively. Use your imagination to picture the scene or enter into it.

2. *What does the Scripture passage mean?*
   Read the footnotes and the commentary to help you understand what the sacred writers intended and what God wanted to communicate by means of their words.

3. *What does the Scripture passage mean to me?*
   Meditate on the passage. God's Word is living and powerful. What is God saying to you today? How does the Scripture passage apply to your life today?

4. *What am I going to do about it?*
Try to discover how God may be challenging you in this passage. An encounter with God contains a challenge to know God's will and follow it more closely in daily life.

THE QUESTIONS ASSIGNED FOR EACH DAY

Read the questions and references for each day. The questions are designed to help you listen to God's Word and to prepare you for the weekly small-group discussion.

Some of the questions can be answered briefly and objectively by referring to the Bible references and the commentary *(What does the passage say?)*. Some will lead you to a better understanding of how the Scriptures apply to the Church, sacraments, and society *(What does the passage mean?)*. Some questions will invite you to consider how God's Word challenges or supports you in your relationships with God and others *(What does the passage mean to me?)*. Finally, the questions will lead you to examine your actions in light of Scripture *(What am I going to do about it?)*.

Write your responses in this study guide or in a notebook to help you clarify and organize your thoughts and feelings.

THE WEEKLY SMALL-GROUP MEETING

The weekly small-group sharing is the heart of the Little Rock Scripture Study Program. Participants gather in small groups to share the results of praying, reading, and reflecting on Scripture and on the assigned questions. The goal of the discussion is for group members to be strengthened and nourished individually and as a community through sharing how God's Word speaks to them and affects their daily lives. The daily study questions will guide the discussion; it is not necessary to discuss all the questions.

All members share the responsibility of creating an atmosphere of loving support and trust in the group by respecting the opinions and experiences of others, and by affirming and encouraging one another. The simple shared prayer which begins and ends each small group meeting also helps create the open and trusting environment in which group members can share their faith deeply and grow in the study of God's Word.

A distinctive feature of this program is its emphasis on and trust in God's presence working in and through each member. Sharing responses to God's presence in the Word and in others can bring about remarkable growth and transformation.

THE WRAP-UP LECTURE

The lecture is designed to develop and clarify the themes of each lesson. It is not intended to be the focus of the group's discussion. For this reason, the lecture always occurs *after* the small group discussion. If several small groups meet at one time, the groups may gather in a central location to listen to the lecture.

Lectures may be presented by a local speaker. They are also available in audio form on cassette or CD, and in visual form on cassette or DVD.

Luke I

NCBC-NT VOLUME 3, PAGES 5–16

Day I

1. What are some of the central ideas (literary motifs) the author of the commentary says are found in Luke (see p. 7)?

2. What is Luke's purpose for writing this gospel (1:1-4)?

3. What is it about the name "Theophilus" that allows all readers to understand themselves to be personally addressed by Luke's Gospel (1:1-4)?

Day 2

4. Who were Elkanah and Hannah and how is their story similar to that of Zechariah and Elizabeth (1:5-25)? (See 1 Sam 1:1-23.)

5. When has the birth of a child brought joy and gladness to you or those you love (1:14)?

6. What will John do that is in the spirit and power of Elijah (1:16-17)? (See 3:3; Mal 3:23-24.)

Day 3

7. How does the annunciation scene differ in Luke (1:26-38) and Matthew? (See Matt 1:18-25.)

8. Gabriel tells Mary not to be troubled, for she has found favor with God (1:30).

    a) Identify some others who found favor with God. (See Exod 33:12-13; 1 Sam 2:26; Prov 3:34; 12:2; 14:9; Isa 60:10; Luke 2:40.)

    b) What signs can you find in your own life that you have found favor with God? (See Prov 8:35.)

9. How do Gabriel's announcements to Zechariah and Mary express recognition of some significant differences between John and Jesus (1:13-17, 30-37)?

Day 4

10. What are the "great reversals" to be worked by God, as proclaimed by Mary in the Magnificat (or Canticle of Mary) (1:46-55)?

11. Have you ever experienced or witnessed a "great reversal" that calls forth praise to God (1:50-53)?

12. What are some different ways you consider Mary to be blessed (1:48)?

Day 5

13. Why do Elizabeth's family and friends come to see John eight days after his birth (1:59)? (See Lev 12:2-3.)

14. What does Zechariah do that apparently returns his power of speech (1:62-64)?

15. What blessings in the lives of friends or family have led to discussions throughout your community (1:65-66)?

Day 6

16. What would you include in a list of praises for what God has done (1:67-79)?

17. a) What does Zechariah tell his son will be his role in God's plan of salvation (1:76-77)?

    b) How might Christians emulate John the Baptist in their daily lives without going to his extremes of appearance or behavior?

18. What does it mean to you to have your feet guided "into the path of peace" (1:79)?

Luke 2

NCBC-NT VOLUME 3, PAGES 16–22

Day 1

1. From last week's lesson, how would you describe the moods or feelings of the people who have witnessed these new developments in God's plan of salvation?

2. What are some of the problems of fixing a date for Christ's birth using the information supplied by Luke (2:1-2)?

3. Joseph and Mary had to travel to Joseph's ancestral home for a census. If you had to return to an ancestral home, where would you have to go? (You may go as far back as you wish, on any side of your family.)

Day 2

4. Why is it important that Jesus be both of the house of David and born in Bethlehem (2:4-7)? (See 1 Sam 17:12; 2 Chr 13:5; Ps 89:4-5; Isa 11:10; Mic 5:1; Matt 2:4-6; Mark 10:46-47; Rom 1:1-3.)

5. Compare traditional depictions of the inn and manger with the description and explanation offered in the commentary. How do they differ?

6. a) Who were typical shepherds of Jesus' time (2:8-14)?

   b) Why might the angels' appearance to shepherds be a significant reflection of much of Luke's theology? (See 7:37-50; 8:1-3, 43-48; 9:47-48; 10:38-42; 13:11-13, 20-22; 15:8-10; 18:16-17; 23:27, 49, 55; 24:9-11.)

Day 3

7. In Scripture, who typically uses the phrase, "do not be afraid," or "fear not" (2:9)? (See 1:13, 30; Gen 15:1; Isa 41:10; Jer 30:10; Dan 10:12; Matt 28:5, 10; Mark 6:50; Acts 27:23-24.)

8. When during Mass are you most likely to encounter the angel's song of praise at Jesus' birth (2:14)?

9. What moments in your life has God touched in such a way that you have kept them to ponder in your heart (2:19)?

Day 4

10. What three different Jewish rites has Luke brought together in the account of the presentation of the infant Jesus at the Temple (2:22-32)? (See Exod 13:2; Lev 12:2-5.)

11. Simeon had been waiting to see the Messiah before he died (2:23). What are some things you most hope God will allow you to see in your lifetime?

12. How do Simeon's words to Mary introduce the theme of schism into Luke's Gospel (2:34-35)?

Day 5

13. In what ways do you see Jesus as a sign of contradiction in modern times and contemporary society (2:34-35)?

14. Simeon and Anna were quite old when they most eloquently proclaimed their faith in Jesus (2:22-38). Who are some of the elderly in your life whose faith bears (or bore) special witness to Christ?

15. Besides Anna, who are some other female prophets mentioned in the Bible (2:36)? (See Exod 15:20; Judg 4:4-9; 2 Kgs 22:14-20; Acts 21:8-9.)

Day 6

16. Why would Joseph and Mary go to Jerusalem to celebrate the Passover (2:41)? (See Deut 16:5-6.)

17. How long was Jesus lost to his parents and what significance is there to the length of time (2:46)? (See 9:22; 24:46.)

18. What kind of childhood and upbringing did Jesus have, according to Luke (2:39-52)?

Ask x Light for the day

- Thank continuously x ev/th.

- What feelings?

      Focus on one   } conscience

      Present to Jesus   } exam.

Ponder - Keep / Learn / mature

Luke 3–5

NCBC-NT VOLUME 3, PAGES 23–41

Day 1

1. What event associated with Jesus' birth or childhood opened up for you in a new way following last week's study?

2. How do the passages from Isaiah help explain the importance of John the Baptist's mission in relation to Jesus (3:4-6)? (See 7:28; Isa 40:3-5.)

3. How could John's warning to the crowds also be taken as a warning to ourselves (3:7-9)?

Day 2

4. John the Baptist gives practical advice to various people who ask for his spiritual direction (3:10-14). What practical advice do you think he might have given you?

5. The people who come to John for baptism are filled with expectation (3:15). What emotions do you recall having at a baptism you might have attended or even received?

6. In Luke the voice from heaven is a private message to Jesus (3:21-22), in Matthew the voice speaks to the crowds (though the message is basically the same). How might the private message convey a special meaning to Jesus?

Day 3

7. What are some important features of Luke's genealogy of Jesus (3:23-38)?

8. How are the temptations of Jesus linked to the wandering of the Israelites following the Exodus (4:1-13)? (See Num 14:26-34.)

9. How does the order in which the temptations of Jesus appear in Luke reflect an important theme in Luke's theology (4:1-13)? (See 9:51; 22:39-46; 24:46-47; Matt 4:1-11.)

He grew in grace & love of the Father
WISDOM

Signals the Kingdom of Heaven
Believe the good news. — Imp. for soul

Do not steal or lie. Pray.
The Charisms & acceptance of fav. of H.
= w/ you I am <u>well pleased</u> —

- bread & Mana
- Kingdoms — possession of land
- power & glory ✗ love of that

promised

Day 4

10. Why were the people of Nazareth unwilling to accept Jesus' ministry and how does Jesus respond (4:16-30)?

11. The commentary calls the scene at Capernaum the beginning of a battle. What is the nature of the battle (4:31-37)? (See 10:18-19.)

12. Why is Jesus said to have "rebuked" the fever of Simon's (Peter's) mother-in-law (4:38-39, 41)?

Day 5

13. Has Peter simply been blessed with a large catch of fish, or is something more being suggested by his catch (5:6-10)?

14. a) How is the response of the first disciples to Jesus' call a model of perfect discipleship (5:11)?

    b) What have you had to leave behind, give up, or cease pursuing in order to follow Jesus?

15. If, like the leper, the report of what Jesus has done for you were to be spread about, what would the report contain (5:12-16)? (See Rom 5:8-11.)

Day 6

16. Why does Jesus tell the man who comes to him for healing of paralysis that his sins are forgiven (5:17-26)? (See John 9:1-3.)

17. How might (or does) your own faith community reach out to those sinners whom Jesus said he came to call (5:27-32)?

18. Jesus says the Good News is like new wine, requiring fresh wine-skins (5:37-39). How can the two thousand-year-old message of the gospel still be called a "new" message?

Luke 6–7

NCBC-NT VOLUME 3, PAGES 41–53

Day 1

1. What stands out for you from Luke's account of the call of the first disciples or the early stages of Jesus' ministry?

2. How does David's eating the forbidden bread help Jesus explain the correctness of what his disciples have done on the Sabbath (6:1-5)? (See 1 Sam 21:1-7; Mark 2:27-28.)

3. Jesus appears to violate the laws concerning work on the Sabbath when real human needs are concerned (6:1-5).

   a) What are the consequences for Jesus and his followers?

   b) Do modern acts of civil disobedience meet the same or similar criteria for breaking laws?

Day 2

4. Jesus prayed with considerable intensity before choosing the twelve apostles (6:12-16). What decisions in your life have you prepared for with much prayer?

5. When have you experienced or witnessed in some way the blessedness Jesus says belongs to the poor, the hungry, the weeping, or those who are persecuted because of their faith in Christ (6:20-23)?

6. How do the beatitudes (6:20-23) reflect "the great reversal theme" that is also found in Mary's canticle (the Magnificat)? (See 1:46-55.)

Day 3

7. What parts of Jesus' Sermon on the Plain do you think meet with the greatest resistance or doubt today (6:20-49)?

8. Who are those in your life who seem to most faithfully live by the golden rule (6:31)?

9. When Jesus says to love your enemies (6:27, 35), does it mean to accept any harm they might wish to do? (See 6:29; Matt 10:16.)

Day 4

10. What are some of the gifts you have been given that you can also give to others (6:38)?

11. How would you describe the essential foundations on which you have built your life (6:46-49)?

12. It is hard to change foundations once a house is built. Can people rebuild their spiritual foundations later in life (6:46-49)?

Day 5

13. What possible embarrassment does the centurion attempt to spare Jesus by telling him he has no need to come to the centurion's home (7:1-10)?

14. How is Jesus' healing of the widow's son reminiscent of the work of an Old Testament prophet (7:11-17)? (See 2 Kgs 4:8-37.)

15. What special importance could the early church attach to the question John the Baptist sends his followers to ask Jesus (7:18-23)? (See Acts 19:1-5.)

Day 6

16. Jesus gives an interesting response to John the Baptist's question (7:18-23). What message would Jesus' response have conveyed to John? (See Isa 29:18-19; 35:5-6; 61:1.)

17. How does the account of the dinner at the Pharisee's home (7:36-48) fit in with Jesus' assertion that there were people claiming Jesus was "a glutton and a drunkard" (7:34)?

18. How has your sense of being forgiven affected your sense of love for Jesus (7:40-50)?

Luke 8–9:50

NCBC-NT VOLUME 3, PAGES 54–69

Day 1

1. Drawing from last week's lesson, what parable, teaching, or event from Jesus' ministry stands out for you? Why does it?

2. How are the women who accompanied Jesus significant to Luke's Gospel (8:1-3)?

3. Where in your own faith community have you noticed the seed that is the Word take root and bear fruit (8:11-15)?

Day 2

4. Which of the many parables or teachings of Jesus would you most like to ask him to explain, as he did for the disciples (8:9-10)?

5. How does the parable of the sower tell us that the Word of God is more than just information to be understood (8:4-15)?

6. What is the "more" that will be given to those who already have (8:16-18)? (See 8:10.)

Day 3

7. a) Why does Jesus seem to prefer the crowd to his mother and other family members (8:19-21)? (See 1:38; 2:51.)

   b) How did Jesus' teaching about family challenge the ideas and customs of his time?

8. The disciples feared perishing in the storm even though they were sailing with Jesus (8:22-25). How have times of crisis affected your faith?

9. How is the spread of the gospel to the Gentiles anticipated by Jesus' exorcism of the man whose demons were called "Legion" (8:26-39)?

Day 4

10. If you were to "return home and recount what God has done for you" in your life (8:39), what would the highlights be?

11. Why did the woman specifically touch Jesus on the tassel of his cloak (8:40-48)? (See Num 15:38.)

12. Jesus sent the Twelve out to proclaim the kingdom of God (9:1-6). (See Matt 10:5-7.) In what various ways does your local faith community exercise its power to proclaim the kingdom of God to the wider community?

Day 5

13. Who might have been a source for some of Herod's information about Jesus (9:7-9)? (See 8:2-3.)

14. a) What are some "eucharistic overtones" found in Luke's account of the feeding of the five thousand (9:10-17)? (See 24:30.)

    b) How does Luke connect the feeding of the five thousand both to Pentecost and to the "eschatological banquet" (9:10-17)? (See Isa 25:6; Acts 2:1-21.)

15. Peter professed faith in Jesus as the Messiah of God (9:18-21). Christians profess faith in Jesus as Lord, God, and Messiah (Christ) every time the creed is recited. What are some other titles and roles that describe or proclaim who Jesus is for you? (See Isa 9:5; Mal 3:20; Matt 1:23; 14:33; Luke 9:22; 18:38; John 1:1, 29; 6:35; 10:14; Col 1:15, 18; 1 Tim 1:17; 1 Pet 2:25; Rev 1:8; 5:5.)

Day 6

16. What does the transfiguration of Jesus teach us about our own discipleship (9:28-36)?

17. What are some practical ways a Christian might serve others as the "least among all of you" (9:46-48)? (See Eph 4:1-3; Phil 2:3-4; 1 Pet 3:8.)

18. Name some examples of those who are "for" Christ even though they might not "follow in our company" (9:49-50).

Luke 9:51–11:54

NCBC-NT VOLUME 3, PAGES 69–84

Day 1

1. What teaching or deed of Jesus found in last week's lesson seems particularly significant or memorable to you?

2. Why would Jesus' determination to go to Jerusalem result in the Samaritan refusal to welcome him (9:51-55)? (See John 4:9, 20.)

3. What challenges does the call to follow Jesus present in your own life (9:57-62)? (See 9:23-24; 14:27; Matt 10:37-39.)

Day 2

4. Comparing the mission of the seventy [-two] (10:1-12) with the mission of the Twelve (9:1-6), which mission would you rather have been a part of and why?

5. a) What are some ways of raising awareness of the abundance of the harvest today (10:2)?

   b) What are some ways for lay people to help labor in the harvest? (See 2 Thess 1:11.)

6. How does Jesus respond to the enthusiasm of the seventy [-two] when they return from their mission (5:19-23)?

Day 3

7. Why is the passage in Luke where Jesus describes his role in making the Father known (5:19-23) said to resemble John's Gospel more than Luke's? (See John 5:19-23; 14:8-10.)

8. Why is loving your neighbor as yourself so closely related to the love that we owe God (10:25-28)? (See Gen 1:26; 1 John 4:12.)

9. a) How would you describe your own experience of being a neighbor?

   b) How does Jesus' teaching concerning being a neighbor challenge you in the midst of your own experience as a neighbor (10:29-37)?

Day 4

10. Why is Mary's choice a better one than Martha's (10:38-42)?

11. How does Luke's version of the Lord's Prayer suggest a different or new understanding of the prayer to you (11:1-4)? (See Matt 6:9-15.)

12. What are some needs you think the Christian community should be persistently praying for (11:9-13)? (See 10:2; 1 Tim 2:1-4; John 17:20-21.)

Day 5

13. What is a key difference between Luke's version of how Jesus taught the need for persistence in prayer (11:9-13) and Matthew's? (See Matt 7:7-11.)

14. What is the great importance of Jesus' power to expel demons (11:14-20)?

15. A woman blessed the womb that bore Jesus (11:27-28). What was Jesus trying to teach by his response to her?

Day 6

16. How is the sign of Jonah in 11:29-32 different from the sign of Jonah in Matthew 12:39-40?

17. What are some important aspects of light and the ability to see light that make it such a powerful symbol for knowledge of God's will (11:33-36)?

18. What challenges to those who teach religion and religious practices do you see in Jesus' rebuke of the scholars of the law (11:45-54)?

Luke 12–13

NCBC-NT VOLUME 3, PAGES 85–96

Day 1

1. What is something memorable to you from last week's lesson?

2. What is unusual about how Jesus refers to the disciples in 12:4? (See Wis 7:24-27; John 15:13-15.)

3. a) What opportunities do you have to acknowledge Jesus before others (12:8-9)? (See Matt 25:31-46.)

   b) Why is public acknowledgement of faith in Jesus important?

Day 2

4. Why does Jesus refuse to settle the dispute between brothers over an inheritance (12:13-15)?

5. How does the parable of the rich fool provide a lesson, or answer, to the brothers disputing an inheritance (12:13-21)?

6. Why might it be significant that the birds God feeds are called ravens (or, perhaps, crows) (12:27)?

Day 3

7. What things in life do you tend to worry about most and how does the gospel challenge you in regard to your concerns (12:22-34)?

8. What would it mean in your life to "gird your loins" and to have your "lamps" lit (12:35-40)?

9. What are some of the special responsibilities with which the Lord has entrusted you (12:41-48)?

Day 4

10. What are some of the different images and meanings of "fire" (12:49) that are mentioned by Luke? (See 3:9, 16-17; 9:54; 17:29; Acts 2:1-4.)

11. Has faith in Christ ever caused discord in relationships in your life (12:51-53)?

12. Can you recall a time in your life when you were able to settle a matter "on the way" with someone before it reached an unsavory conclusion (12:57-59)?

Day 5

13. How well is Jesus' own ministry within Israel reflected in the parable of the fig tree and the gardener (13:6-9)?

14. How does Jesus justify his healing of the infirm woman on the Sabbath (13:10-17)? (See 6:9.)

15. a) What do the similes of the mustard seed and the leaven have in common (13:18-21)?

 b) What do they teach about the kingdom of God?

Day 6

16. Why is the warning to enter through "the narrow gate" considered a warning against attachment to earthly goods and possessions (13:23-30)?

17. Where in Jesus' message to Herod is a reference to Jesus' impending death and resurrection (13:31-33)?

18. a) What must happen if Jerusalem is to see Jesus (13:35)? (See 19:38.)

 b) What do the people actually say when Jesus finally enters Jerusalem (19:38)?

 c) When are much the same words recited by the people in Catholic liturgy?

Luke 14–16

NCBC-NT VOLUME 3, PAGES 97–112

Day 1

1. Which of Jesus' teachings, parables, or deeds found in last week's lesson stand out most clearly for you now?

2. What do Jesus' actions on the Sabbath reveal about the true purpose of the Sabbath (14:1-6)? (See 13:10-17; Mark 2:23-28; John 5:1-17.)

3. a) What are some activities and events in your area where status and celebrity have become important factors (14:7-14)?

   b) What kind of events could be celebrated in your area that might highlight the dignity of the poor or otherwise marginalized members of the community?

Day 2

4. Why were the excuses of the people who would not attend the dinner unacceptable (14:15-24)?

5. How could "hating" one's closest family members ever be considered necessary to following Jesus (14:26)?

6. What is a cross you have been asked to bear (14:27)?

Day 3

7. What are some aspects of your faith community's presence in the larger community that you think might be described as salt (14:34-35)?

8. In the parable of the lost coin, what does the coin seem to represent and what does the woman represent (15:8-10)?

9. Why is there more rejoicing over the repentant sinner than over the righteous (15:7, 10)? (See 7:36-48; Ezek 33:11-19.)

Day 4

10. a) How does the father show that he had never rejected the younger child as well as assure the older child that he has always been loved (15:11-32)?

    b) How have you experienced in some way the events or teachings of this parable (15:11-32)?

11. a) In spite of his serious faults, what does the dishonest steward do that makes him like Jesus (16:1-8a)?

    b) What has the dishonest steward done to win praise from his master, and what does that teach us (16:1-8a)?

12. How does Jesus' teaching concerning the use of wealth challenge you (16:8b-13)?

Day 5

13. Besides overvaluing material wealth, what are some things that are highly esteemed in modern cultures that might also be "an abomination in the sight of God" (16:14-15)?

14. How does the commentary explain Jesus' statements concerning entering the kingdom of God by violence (16:16)? (See Matt 11:12.)

15. a) How has Jesus' teaching on marriage and divorce been a historical means of protection for women and children (16:18)?

    b) How has Jesus' teaching on marriage and divorce presented dilemmas in modern parish life?

Day 6

16. a) Where does Jesus say the angels carry Lazarus (16:22)?

    b) What separates the rich man (traditionally referred to as "Dives") from Lazarus?

17. What could the rich man have done to avoid his fate (16:26)?

18. a) What do the Law (Moses) and the Prophets have to say about the rich and the poor (16:29-31)? (See Exod 22:21-22; Deut 10:17-19; 24:20-22; Jer 7:5; Isa 58:5-7.)

    b) How do these teachings challenge you?

Luke 17–19

NCBC-NT VOLUME 3, PAGES 112–128

Day One

1. What is something from last week's lesson that has remained with you since then?

2. How would you go about challenging the moral conduct of a friend who had strayed (17:3)?

3. The apostles asked Jesus to increase their faith (17:5). What has the Lord done in your life that has increased your faith?

Day 2

4. How does a humble acknowledgment that one is an "unprofitable servant" differ from having a negative self-concept or an unhealthy contempt for oneself (17:7-10)?

5. What all did the Samaritan leper gain as a result of his faith (17:11-19)? (See 7:50; 8:48; 23:43.)

6. What are some different ways of understanding what Jesus meant by saying "the kingdom of God is among you" (17:21)? (See NAB footnotes; 11:20.)

Day 3

7. a) What does Jesus say about the coming of the Son of Man that warns against designating a particular time for his return (17:22-36)?

   b) What does he say to caution against believing that it is too far off in the future to worry about (17:22-36)?

8. How is the widow in the story of the disrespectful judge like Christ (18:1-8)?

9. The theme of "reversal" is prevalent in Luke. How does the parable of the Pharisee and the tax collector at prayer demonstrate this theme at work (18:9-14)? (See 1:52-53; 4:18-19; 9:25; 10:15; 14:11, 16-24; 15:24; 17:33.)

.

Day 4

10. What does it mean to accept the kingdom of God as a child (18:16)?

11. How would you describe the "return" you have received for whatever you have sacrificed in order to follow Jesus (18:29-30)?

12. The disciples could not comprehend Jesus' teaching concerning his own death (18:31-34). What teachings, if any, do you find difficult to understand?

Day 5

13. What is significant about the title, "Son of David," that the blind beggar calls Jesus (18:35-43)? (See Jer 33:17; Ps 89:4-5; Isa 11:10.)

14. Zaccheus was a wealthy tax collector (19:1-10). Where does he fit in with Luke's larger message of God's acceptance of the poor, the lowly, and the outcast? (See 4:18-19; 14:15-24; 15:1-7; 18:24.)

15. What will be given "to everyone who has," but will be taken away "from the one who has not" (19:11-27)? (See 8:18.)

Day 6

16. How does Luke's description of Jesus' entry into Jerusalem set itself apart from those found in the other gospels (19:37-38)? (See Matt 21:8-11; Mark 11:8-10; John 12:12-13.)

17. What historical event is probably being referred to in Jesus' lament over Jerusalem (19:41-44)?

18. a) How has Luke's portrayal of the cleansing of the Temple (19:45-46) created a gentler description than found in the other gospels? (See Matt 21:12-13; Mark 11:15-17; John 2:14-16.)

    b) How much danger do you see today of confusing our houses of worship with the objectives of the marketplace (19:25)?

Luke 20–22

NCBC-NT VOLUME 3, PAGES 128–144

Day 1

1. What has made the strongest impression on you from last week's lesson?

2. In your own words, how would you summarize Luke's depiction of the good news that Jesus would have proclaimed in the Temple area (20:1)?

3. Why is the question of Jesus' authority for his words and deeds of such importance and also dangerous for Jesus to answer (20:1-8)? (See 5:23-24; Matt 7:28-29.)

Day 2

4. What does the parable of the tenant farmers and the owner of the vineyard reveal about how Jesus is being received (20:9-18)?

5. What does Jesus' teaching to "repay to Caesar what belongs to Caesar and to God what belongs to God" (20:20-26) imply about the relationship between civic duties and obligations of faith?

6. What is the Jewish religious obligation alluded to in 20:27-40? (See Deut 25:5-10.)

Day 3

7. When have you been particularly comforted by the knowledge that to God, "all are alive" (20:38)?

8. How might the accusation against the scribes, that "they devour the houses of widows," put a different slant on the account of the widow who "put in more than all the rest" (20:45–21:4)? (See Mark 12:38-44.)

9. When Luke was written, the destruction of the Temple had already occurred. What purpose(s) might the inclusion of Jesus' prediction of its destruction have served his first readers (21:5-6)?

Day 4

10. Does Jesus name any signs for his followers that can be used to help determine the time of his return (21:7-36)?

11. Are there any special factors in our times that might distract us from the need for vigilance as we await the coming of the Lord (21:36)?

12. Why would the Passover have been important to Jesus and his disciples (22:7–13)? (See Exod 12:11-17, 26-27, 29-32.)

Day 5

13. a) What did Jesus identify with the bread and the second cup of the last meal he shared with his disciples (22:14-20)?

    b) How has Jesus' gift of himself in this meal made a difference in your own life?

14. What are some of the opportunities you have been given to be among the people of God as one who serves (22:27)?

15. How does the warning Jesus gives Simon Peter about his forthcoming denial also reveal a special role Peter will have among the apostles in the future (22:31-34)? (See Acts 1:15; 2:14; 11:1-18.)

Day 6

16. Jesus prayed in the garden, "Father, if you are willing, take this cup away from me; still, not my will but yours be done" (22:42). When have you seen something good come out of a situation you may have wished to avoid (22:39-46)?

17. Peter heard the cock crow and remembered "the word of the Lord." Has the word of the Lord, or a passage of Scripture, ever leaped to your mind as an insight to or reflection on a situation (22:61-62)?

18. Why does Jesus not answer the Sanhedrin plainly when they ask him if he is the Messiah (22:66-71)?

Luke 23–24

NCBC-NT VOLUME 3, PAGES 145–158

Day 1

1. Of the many events of Jesus' last days covered in last week's lesson, which do you think would have been most difficult or troubling for Jesus?

2. a) In all, the "whole assembly" present Pilate with three charges against Jesus. What are they (23:1-4)?

   b) Which charge receives the most emphasis?

3. a) How does Luke emphasize Jesus' innocence during his trial (23:1-22)?

   b) What finally convinces Pilate that he should sentence Jesus to death (23:1-25)?

Day 2

4. During his trial, Jesus was mocked by Herod and his soldiers and Pilate ultimately ignored his innocence (23:11, 22-24). How has your faith in Jesus been put on trial?

5. Simon carried Jesus' cross for him (23:26). Have you ever felt called upon to carry a burden (concern or need) for Christ?

6. Those who taunt Jesus admit that he saved others (23:35). What are some of the ways Jesus demonstrates his desire to save others even after being sentenced to death by Pilate (23:25-46)?

Day 3

7. How do the responses of the two criminals crucified alongside Jesus reflect the "schism" theme found in Luke (23:39-43)? (See 2:34, 51-53.)

8. What is the significance of the veil of the Temple being torn (23:45)? (See Lev 16:1-3.)

9. What action of the onlookers might give reason for believing that they were seeking forgiveness for any role they played in Jesus' crucifixion (23:48)? (See 18:13-14.)

Day 4

10. Why would it be important that Joseph of Arimathea placed Jesus' body in a new tomb (23:50-53)?

11. a) Who are the women in Luke's account that go to the tomb to care for Jesus' body (23:55–24:11)?

    b) Why didn't the apostles believe their report?

12. The women are asked why they seek the living one among the dead (24:5). What are some ways that we might seek the risen one among the living today?

Day 5

13. What evidence supports the claim that the two disciples who met Jesus on the road to Emmaus were a married couple (24:13–35)?

14. The disciples recognized Jesus in the breaking of the bread (24:30-31). What are the several ways Catholics are taught to recognize the presence of Christ in our celebrations of Eucharist?

15. a) How does Jesus demonstrate that he is not a ghost (24:36-42)? (See John 20:24-27.)

    b) Why would it be important that Jesus was not just a ghost? (See 1 Cor 15:13-20.)

Day 6

16. a) What gift did Jesus give the apostles in regard to Sacred Scripture (24:27, 45-47)?

    b) How is this gift still present in your life?

17. How do the closing passages of the Gospel According to Luke prepare the reader for what will follow in the Acts of the Apostles (24:45)? (See Acts 1:1-12; 2:46.)

18. How has your study of Luke's Gospel contributed to your understanding of what is meant by "the Good News"?

NOTES

ABBREVIATIONS

Books of the Bible

Gen—Genesis
Exod—Exodus
Lev—Leviticus
Num—Numbers
Deut—Deuteronomy
Josh—Joshua
Judg—Judges
Ruth—Ruth
1 Sam—1 Samuel
2 Sam—2 Samuel
1 Kgs—1 Kings
2 Kgs—2 Kings
1 Chr—1 Chronicles
2 Chr—2 Chronicles
Ezra—Ezra
Neh—Nehemiah
Tob—Tobit
Jdt—Judith
Esth—Esther
1 Macc—1 Maccabees
2 Macc—2 Maccabees
Job—Job
Ps(s)—Psalm(s)
Prov—Proverbs
Eccl—Ecclesiastes
Song—Song of Songs
Wis—Wisdom
Sir—Sirach
Isa—Isaiah
Jer—Jeremiah
Lam—Lamentations
Bar—Baruch
Ezek—Ezekiel
Dan—Daniel
Hos—Hosea
Joel—Joel
Amos—Amos

Obad—Obadiah
Jonah—Jonah
Mic—Micah
Nah—Nahum
Hab—Habakkuk
Zeph—Zephaniah
Hag—Haggai
Zech—Zechariah
Mal—Malachi
Matt—Matthew
Mark—Mark
Luke—Luke
John—John
Acts—Acts
Rom—Romans
1 Cor—1 Corinthians
2 Cor—2 Corinthians
Gal—Galatians
Eph—Ephesians
Phil—Philippians
Col—Colossians
1 Thess—1 Thessalonians
2 Thess—2 Thessalonians
1 Tim—1 Timothy
2 Tim—2 Timothy
Titus—Titus
Phlm—Philemon
Heb—Hebrews
Jas—James
1 Pet—1 Peter
2 Pet—2 Peter
1 John—1 John
2 John—2 John
3 John—3 John
Jude—Jude
Rev—Revelation